HATS OFF, ANDY CAPP

BY *Smythe*

A FAWCETT GOLD MEDAL BOOK
Fawcett Publications, Inc., Greenwich, Conn.
Member of American Book Publishers Council, Inc.

STEPHEN B. WEINER

'OW D'YER KEEP 'ER AT IT, ANDY?

I JUST TELL 'ER THAT SHE'S GETTIN' TOO OLD F' THAT KIND O' THING

TCH! TCH! THE STATE OF THEM CURTAINS! —AN' THEM WALLS!

AN' THAT CEILIN'!... SOMETHIN' WILL 'AVE TO BE DONE

THERE Y'GO AGAIN — TAKIN' ME CUP AWAY BEFORE I'M FINISHED! YER ALWAYS DOIN' THAT—!

ALL RIGHT, ALL RIGHT, KEEP YER HAIR ON — THERE'S NO NEED FOR YER T' LOSE YER TEMPER

ON

SCREECH

TELEVISION

THAT'S THE TROUBLE WI' TELEVISION — PEOPLE ARE LOSIN' THE ABILITY T' MAKE THEIR OWN AMUSEMENT!

FLO, COULD YER LEND ME —

BLIMEY! I'M 'ARDLY INSIDE THE DOOR BEFORE YOU'RE ASKIN' ME FOR MONEY!

IS IT MY FAULT THAT YOU'RE ARF AN HOUR LATE?!

TCH! I 'OPE NOBODY GOT 'URT! – 'AVE *YOU* EVER BEEN IN A TRAIN CRASH, FLO?

NOT THAT I CAN REMEMBER

NOT THAT YER CAN *REMEMBER*?

AFTER LIVIN' FOR A WHILE WI' ANDY, YER FORGET SUCH TRIFLES

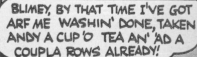

WHAT MADE YER THINK OF THAT, ALL OF A SUDDEN?

RAT-A
TAT-TAT!

OH, BLIMEY, THAT'LL BE ADA JACKSON. TELL 'ER I'M NOT IN — I'M IN NO MOOD F' LISTENIN' TO *ER* CHAT THIS MORNIN'

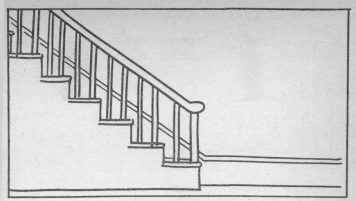

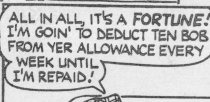

CRAZY. THEY WANT 'OME ATMOSPHERE IN A HOTEL AN' HOTEL SERVICE ROUND THE HOUSE! STILL, OURS IS NOT TO REASON WHY—

I 'OPE YER DON'T MIND ME MENTIONIN' IT, BUT YOU'RE SUPPOSED TO BE A MEMBER OF THE WEAKER SEX!

'E'S RIGHT, Y' KNOW